Contents

A **pull-out answers section** (pages A1 to A8) appears in the centre of this book, between pages 20 and 21. It also gives simple guidance on how best to use this book. Remove this section before you begin working through the tests.

Which picture on the right belongs to the group on the left? Circle the letter.

Example

a b c d e

1. a b c d e

2. a b c d e

3. a b c d e

4. a b c d e

5. a b c d e

6. a b c d e

Now go on to the next page. ➡

■ Which picture is the odd one out? Circle the letter.

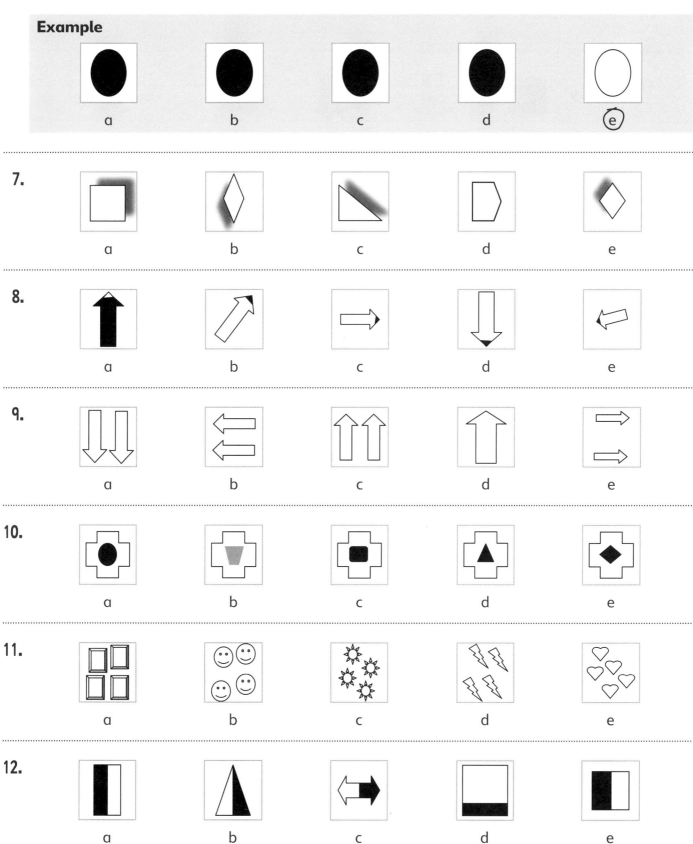

Example

a   b   c   d   e

7.   a   b   c   d   e

8.   a   b   c   d   e

9.   a   b   c   d   e

10.   a   b   c   d   e

11.   a   b   c   d   e

12.   a   b   c   d   e

End of test.

Score:		Time taken:		Target met?	

■ The first two pictures go together. Which of the five pictures on the right goes with the third picture in the same way? Circle the letter.

Example

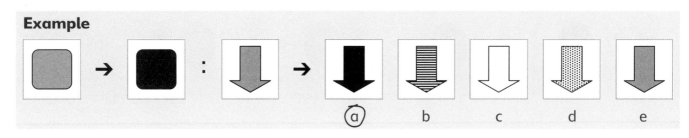

1.

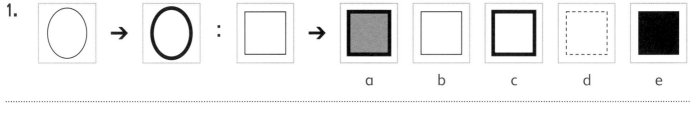

2.

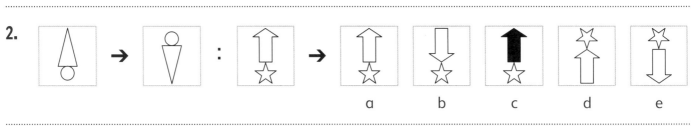

3.

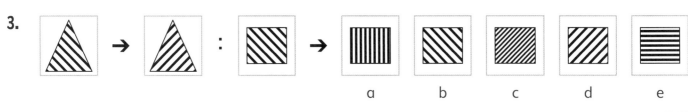

4.

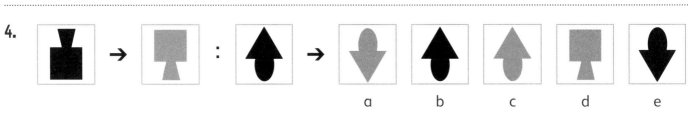

5.

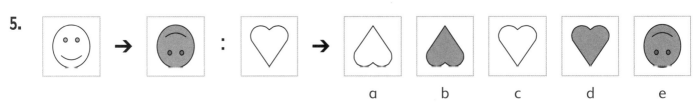

6.

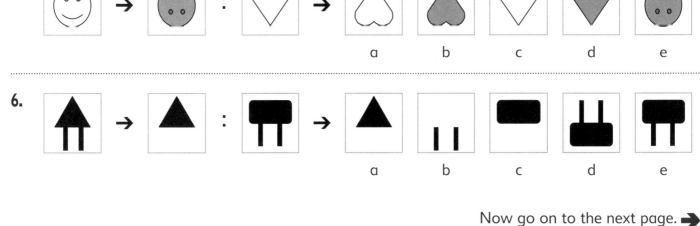

Now go on to the next page. ➡

■ Which picture on the right goes in the empty space? Circle the letter.

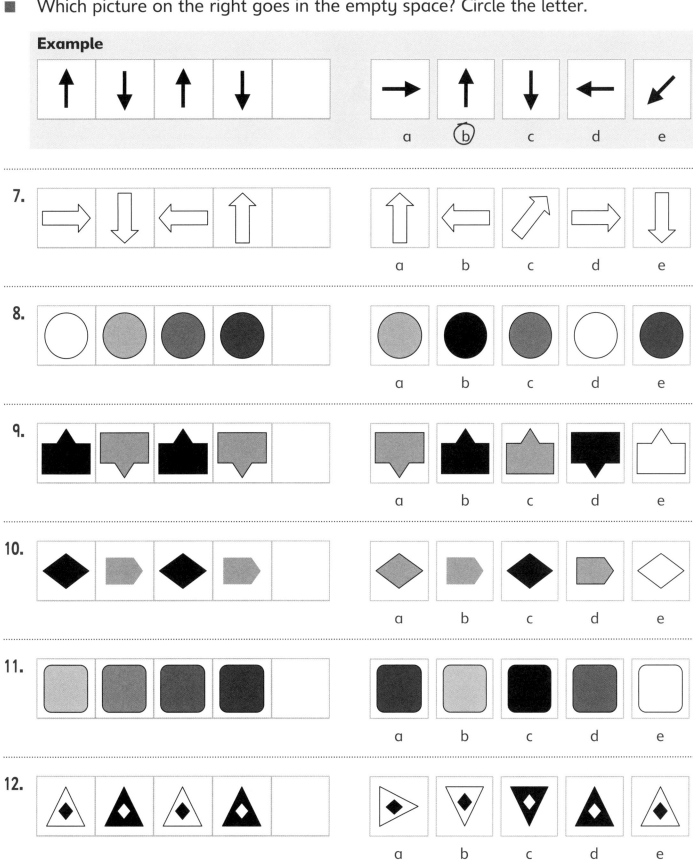

Example

7.

8.

9.

10.

11.

12.

End of test.

Score:	Time taken:	Target met?

Target time: **6 minutes**

In which picture on the right is the picture on the left hidden? Circle the letter.

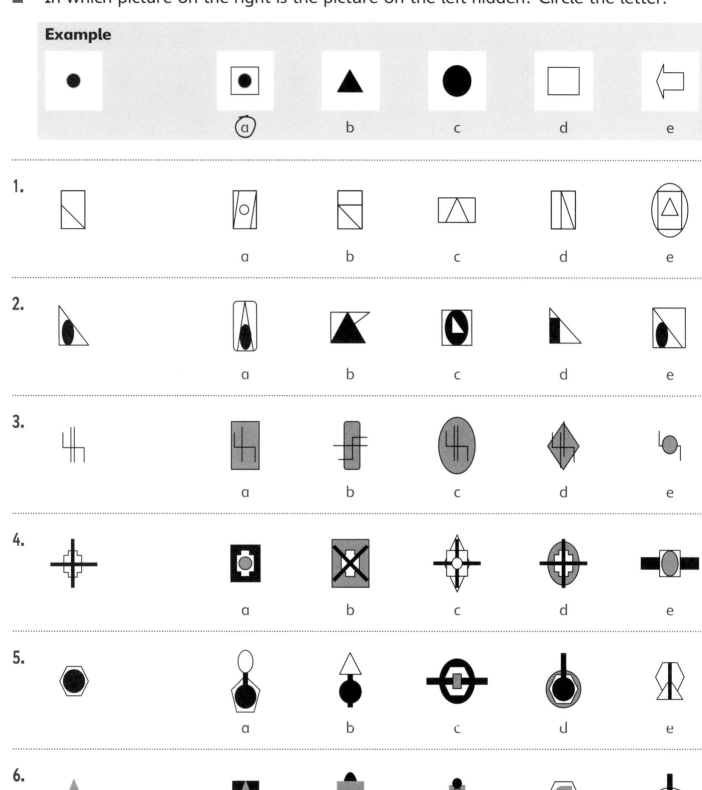

Example

a · b · c · d · e

1. a · b · c · d · e

2. a · b · c · d · e

3. a · b · c · d · e

4. a · b · c · d · e

5. a · b · c · d · e

6. a · b · c · d · e

Now go on to the next page. ➡

■ Pretend the dotted line is a mirror. Which picture on the right is a reflection of the picture on the left? Circle the letter.

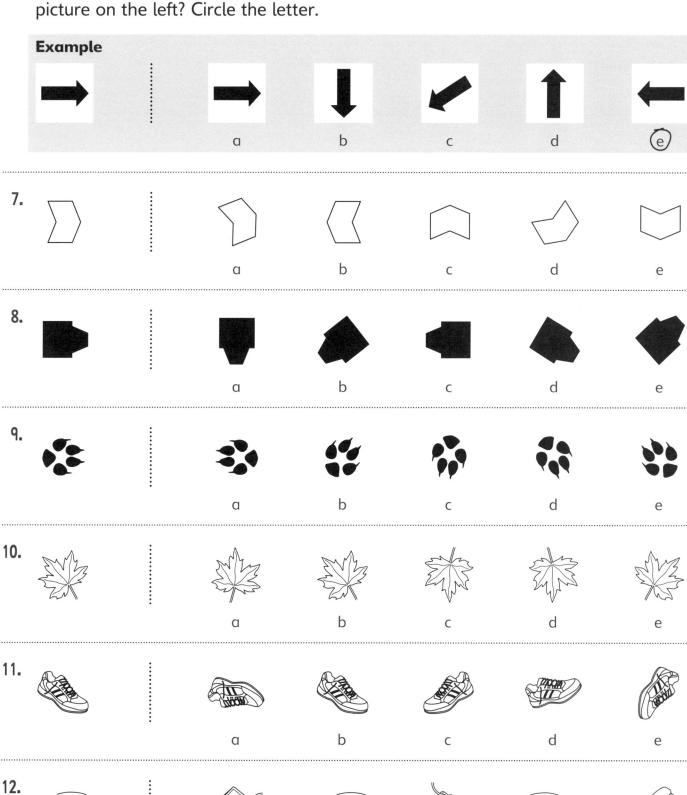

Example

a   b   c   d   (e)

7.   a   b   c   d   e

8.   a   b   c   d   e

9.   a   b   c   d   e

10.   a   b   c   d   e

11.   a   b   c   d   e

12.   a   b   c   d   e

End of test.

Score:		Time taken:		Target met?	

Which of the pictures on the right best fits into the space in the grid?
Circle the letter.

Example

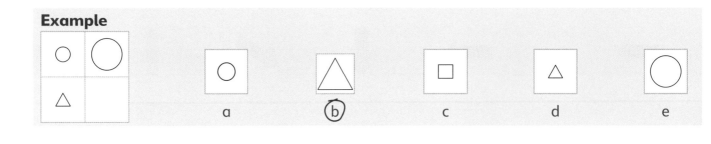

a   b   c   d   e

1.

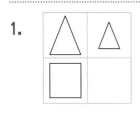

a   b   c   d   e

2.

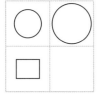

a   b   c   d   e

3.

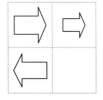

a   b   c   d   e

4.

a   b   c   d   e

5.

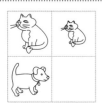

a   b   c   d   e

Now go on to the next page. ➡

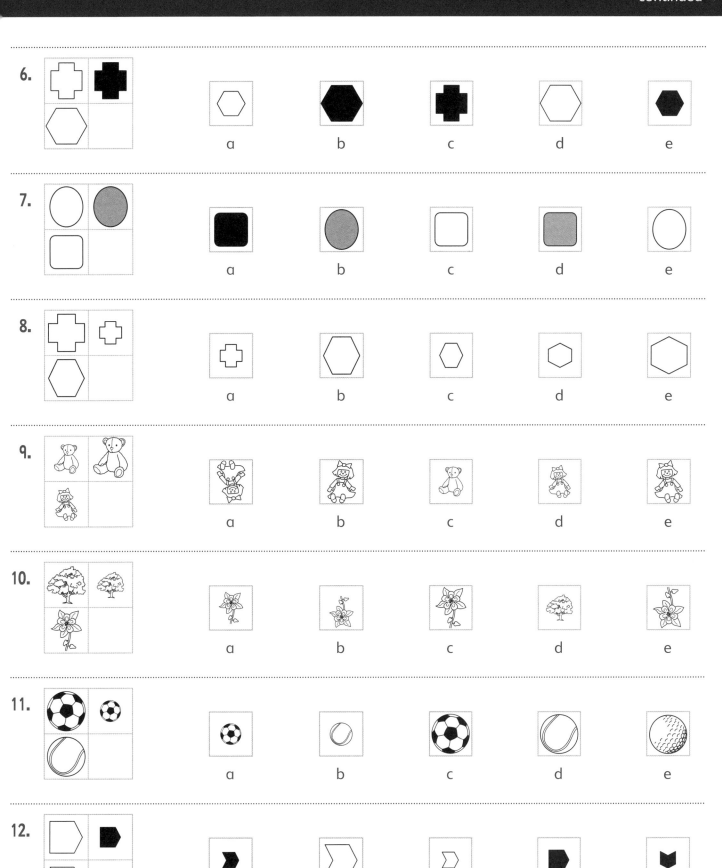

6.

a

b

c

d

e

7.

a

b

c

d

e

8.

a

b

c

d

e

9.

a

b

c

d

e

10.

a

b

c

d

e

11.

a

b

c

d

e

12.

a

b

c

d

e

End of test.

| Score: | | Time taken: | | Target met? | |

Which picture on the right goes in the empty space? Circle the letter.

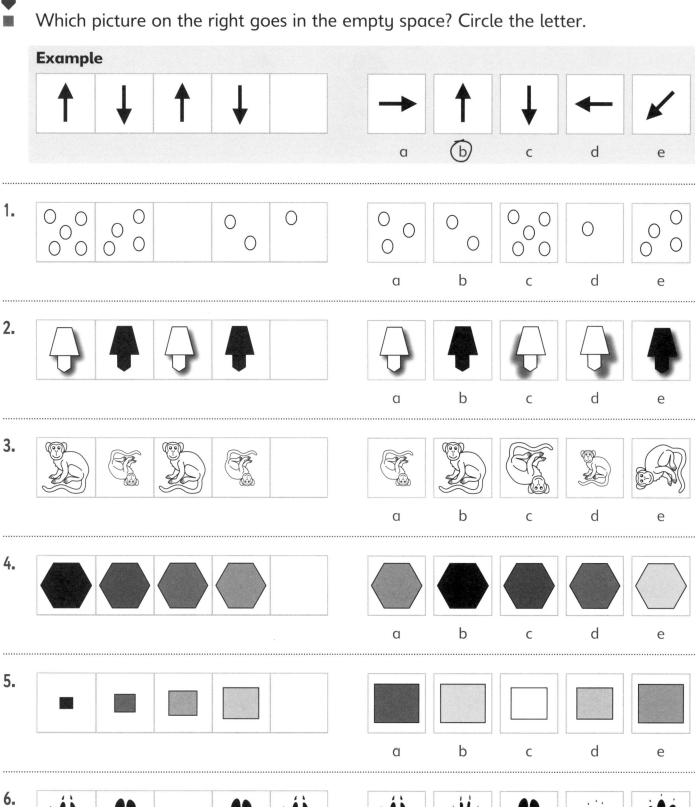

In which picture on the right is the picture on the left hidden? Circle the letter.

Example

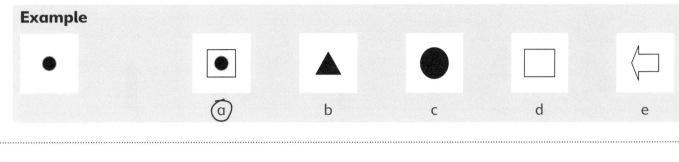

a   b   c   d   e

7.

a   b   c   d   e

8.

a   b   c   d   e

9.

a   b   c   d   e

10.

a   b   c   d   e

11.

a   b   c   d   e

12.

a   b   c   d   e

End of test.

Score:	Time taken:	Target met?

Target time: 6 minutes

Pretend the dotted line is a mirror. Which picture on the right is a reflection of the picture on the left? Circle the letter.

Example

a   b   c   d   (e)

1.

     a   b   c   d   e

2.

     a   b   c   d   e

3.

     a   b   c   d   e

4.

     a   b   c   d   e

5.

     a   b   c   d   e

6.

     a   b   c   d   e

Now go on to the next page. ➔

■ Which of the pictures on the right best fits into the space in the grid?
Circle the letter.

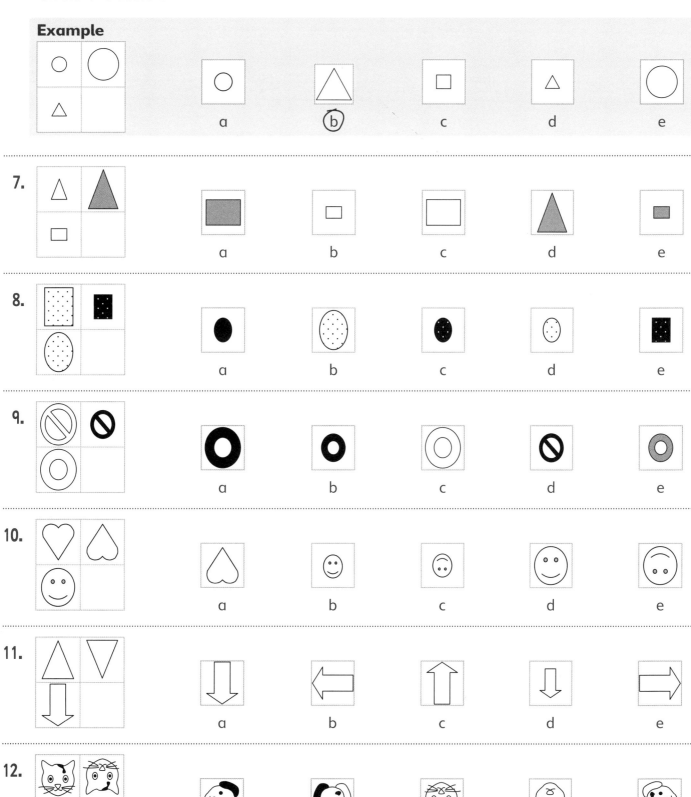

Example

a	b	c	d	e

7.

| a | b | c | d | e |

8.

| a | b | c | d | e |

9.

| a | b | c | d | e |

10.

| a | b | c | d | e |

11.

| a | b | c | d | e |

12.

| a | b | c | d | e |

End of test.

| Score: | Time taken: | Target met? |

Which picture on the right belongs to the group on the left? Circle the letter.

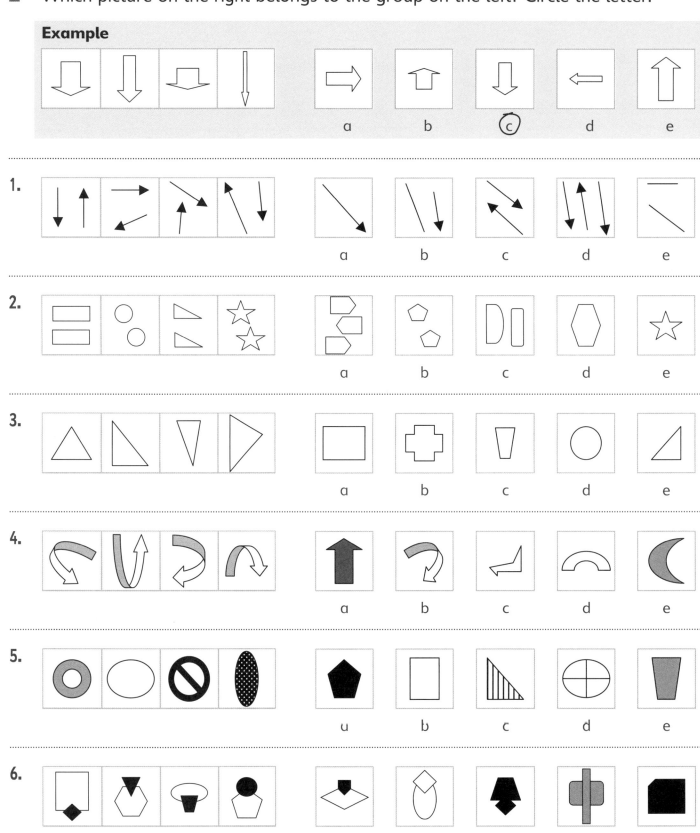

Example

a   b   c   d   e

1.

a   b   c   d   e

2.

a   b   c   d   e

3.

a   b   c   d   e

4.

a   b   c   d   e

5.

u   b   c   d   e

6.

a   b   c   d   e

Now go on to the next page. ➡

■ Which picture is the odd one out? Circle the letter.

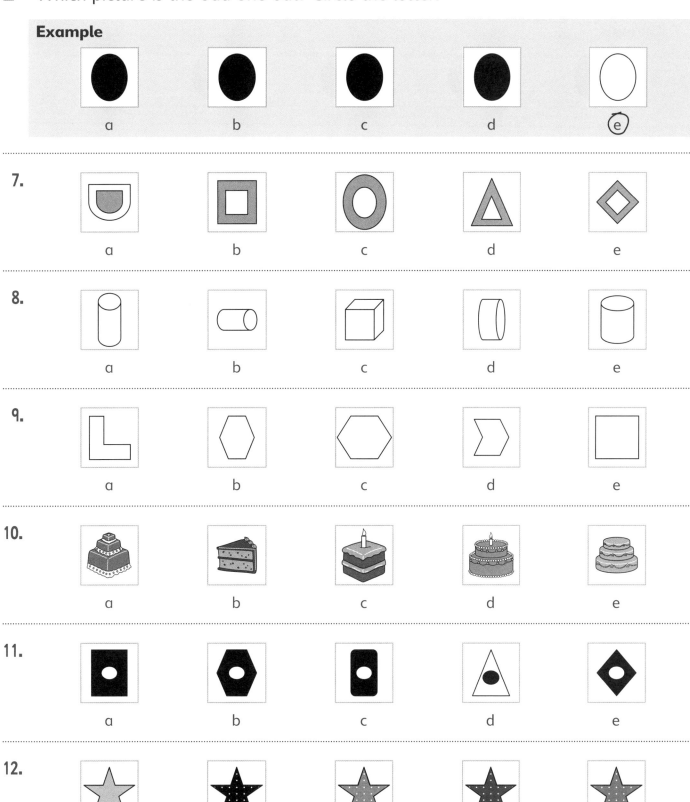

Example

| a | b | c | d | e |

7.

| a | b | c | d | e |

8.

| a | b | c | d | e |

9.

| a | b | c | d | e |

10.

| a | b | c | d | e |

11.

| a | b | c | d | e |

12.

| a | b | c | d | e |

End of test.

| Score: | Time taken: | Target met? |

Target time: **6 minutes**

Which picture is the odd one out? Circle the letter.

Example

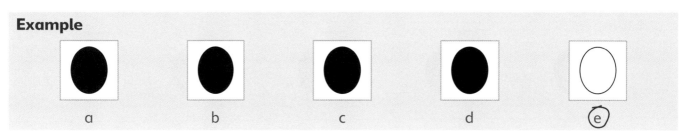

| a | b | c | d | e |

1.

| a | b | c | d | e |

2.

| a | b | c | d | e |

3.

| a | b | c | d | e |

4.

| a | b | c | d | e |

5.

| a | b | c | d | e |

6.

| a | b | c | d | e |

Now go on to the next page. ➡

■ The first two pictures go together. Which of the five pictures on the right goes with the third picture in the same way? Circle the letter.

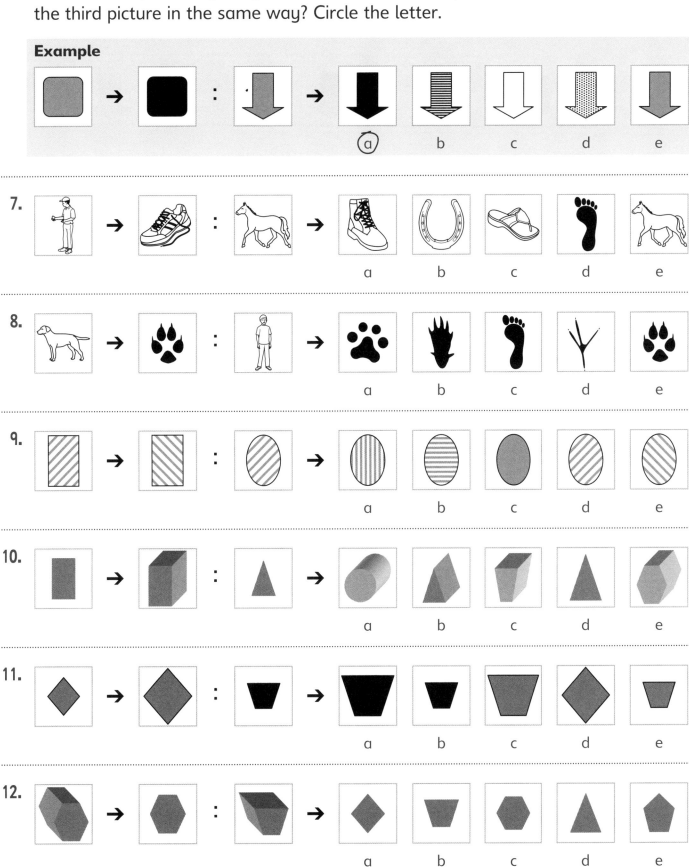

Example

7.

8.

9.

10.

11.

12.

End of test.

Target time: **6 minutes**

The first two pictures go together. Which of the five pictures on the right goes with the third picture in the same way? Circle the letter.

Example

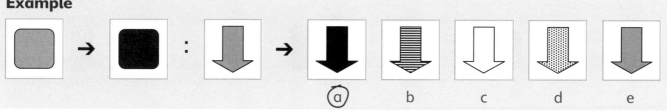

1.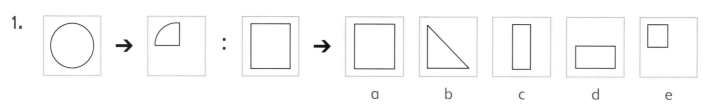

2.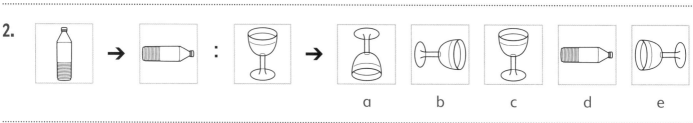

3.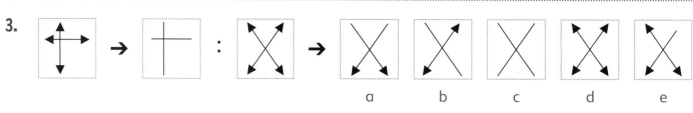

4.

5.

6.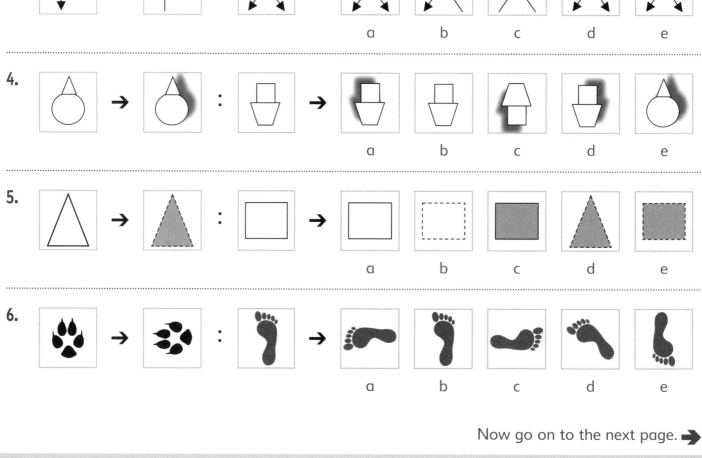

Now go on to the next page. ➡

Notes for parents, tutors, teachers and other adult helpers

- **Non-verbal Reasoning 2** is designed for seven- and eight-year-olds, but may also be suitable for some children of other ages.

- Remove this pull-out section before giving the book to the child.

- Before the child begins work on the first test, together read the instructions headed **What to do** on page 2. As you do so, point out to the child the different elements in **Section 1 Test 1**.

- Make sure that the child understands how to answer multiple choice questions and has a pencil and eraser. Also ensure that the child is able to see a clock or a watch.

- Be sure that the child knows to tell you clearly when he or she has finished the test.

- When the child is ready, say 'Start the test now' and make a note of the start time.

- When the child has finished, make a note of the end time and then work out how long he or she took to complete the test. Then fill in the **Time taken** box, which appears at the end of the test.

- Mark the child's work using this pull-out section, giving one mark for each correct answer. Then complete the **Score** box at the end of the test.

- This table shows you how to mark the **Target met?** box and the **Action** notes help you to plan the next step. However, these are suggestions only. Please use your own judgement as you decide how best to proceed.

Score	Time taken	Target met?	Action
1–6	Any	Not yet	Give the child the previous book in the series. Provide help and support as needed.
7–9	Any	Not yet	Encourage the child to keep practising using the tests in this book. The child may need to repeat some tests. If so, wait a few weeks or the child may simply remember the correct answers. Provide help and support as needed.
10–12	Over target – child took too long	Not yet	
10–12	On target – child took suggested time or less	Yes	Encourage the child to keep practising using further tests in this book, and to move on to the next book when you think this is appropriate.

- Whatever the test score, always encourage the child to have another go at the questions that he or she got wrong – without looking at the solutions. If the child's answers are still incorrect, work through these questions together. Demonstrate the correct method if necessary.

- If the child struggles with particular question types, help him or her to develop the strategies needed.

The **Understanding Reasoning** series, also available from Schofield & Sims, provides clear explanations on how to answer reasoning questions. It also provides 'Tips for tests' and 'Tips for revision'. For further details on this and other series that help children and young people to prepare for school selection tests, and for free downloads relating to the **Rapid Reasoning Tests**, visit www.schofieldandsims.co.uk

Answers

Section 1 Test 1 (pages 4–5)

1. **c** Each picture contains the same shape.
2. **b** Each picture contains a 3D shape.
3. **e** Each picture contains three objects.
4. **c** Each picture contains the same shape.
5. **b** Each picture contains a white shape with a grey trapezium.
6. **b** Each picture contains four ovals.
7. **d** The others all have shadows.
8. **a** The others are all white with a black tip.
9. **d** The others all have two arrows.
10. **b** The others all have a black shape in the centre.
11. **e** The others all have four objects.
12. **d** The others all have half the shape shaded.

Section 1 Test 2 (pages 6–7)

1. **c** The shape stays the same size and colour, but the outline gets thicker.
2. **e** The picture is reflected in the horizontal mirror line.
3. **d** The lines are reflected in the vertical mirror line.
4. **a** The shape is reflected in the horizontal mirror line and changes from black to grey.
5. **b** The picture is reflected in the horizontal mirror line and changes from white to grey.
6. **c** The two lines are taken away.
7. **d** The arrows rotate 90° clockwise.
8. **b** The circles get gradually darker.
9. **b** Repeating pattern
10. **c** Repeating pattern
11. **c** The shape gets darker.
12. **e** Repeating pattern

Section 1 Test 3 (pages 8–9)

1. **b**
2. **e**
3. **c**
4. **d**
5. **d**
6. **a**
7. **b**
8. **c**
9. **a**
10. **e**
11. **c**
12. **d**

Section 1 Test 4 (pages 10–11)

1. **b** The shape gets smaller.
2. **c** The shape gets bigger.
3. **a** The shape gets smaller but is still facing the same way.
4. **c** The picture gets smaller but is still facing the same way.
5. **a** The picture gets smaller but is still facing the same way.
6. **b** The white shape changes to a black shape.
7. **d** The white shape changes to a grey shape.
8. **c** The shape gets smaller.
9. **e** The picture gets bigger but is still facing the same way.
10. **a** The picture gets smaller but is still facing the same way.
11. **b** The picture gets smaller.
12. **a** The shape gets smaller and changes from white to black.

Section 1 Test 5 (pages 12–13)

1. **a** There is one less oval each time.
2. **a** Repeating pattern
3. **b** Repeating pattern
4. **e** The shape gets lighter in colour.
5. **b** The shape gets bigger and lighter in colour.
6. **a** Repeating pattern
7. **c**
8. **d**
9. **e**
10. **b**

11. **c**

12. **d**

Section 1 Test 6 (pages 14–15)

1. **a**
2. **c**
3. **a**
4. **b**
5. **e**
6. **b**

7. **a** The shape gets bigger and changes from white to grey.
8. **c** The shape gets smaller and changes from white with black spots to black with white spots.
9. **b** The picture gets smaller and changes from white to black.
10. **e** The picture is reflected in the horizontal mirror line.
11. **c** The shape is reflected in the horizontal mirror line.
12. **d** The picture is reflected in the horizontal mirror line.

Section 2 Test 1 (pages 16–17)

1. **c** Each picture contains two arrows.
2. **b** Each picture contains two identical shapes.
3. **e** Each picture contains a triangle.
4. **b** Each picture contains a curved arrow.
5. **d** Each picture contains a curved shape.
6. **a** Each picture contains a black shape overlapping a white shape.
7. **a** The others all have a grey outer and a white inner.
8. **c** The others are all cylinders.
9. **e** The others all have six sides.
10. **b** The others are all whole cakes.
11. **d** The others are all black shapes with white ovals inside.
12. **a** The others all have spots.

Section 2 Test 2 (pages 18–19)

1. **a** The others all have an oval.
2. **d** The others all have three rectangles.
3. **a** The others all have stripes going in the same direction.
4. **e** The others are all the same size.
5. **d** The others all have stripes.
6. **c** The others are all curved lines.
7. **b** The type of shoe each wears.
8. **c** This is the print left by the foot.
9. **e** The stripes are reflected.
10. **b** The 2D shape becomes a 3D shape.
11. **a** The shape gets bigger but stays the same colour.
12. **b** The 3D shape becomes a 2D shape.

Section 2 Test 3 (pages 20–21)

1. **e** The shape is quartered.
2. **b** The picture rotates 90° clockwise.
3. **c** All the arrow heads are removed.
4. **d** A shadow appears to the top right.
5. **e** The outer line becomes dotted and the shape changes from white to grey.
6. **a** The picture rotates 90° anticlockwise.
7. **a** Each picture contains a black shape and a grey shape.
8. **b** Each picture contains a double-headed arrow and a single-headed zig-zag arrow.
9. **d** Each picture contains a grey shape inside a white oval.
10. **d** Each picture is half black and half white.
11. **c** Each picture is a rotation of the same shape.
12. **e** Each picture has a rectangle containing two ovals that are both the same colour.

Section 2 Test 4 (pages 22–23)

1. **b**

2. **a**

3. **d**

4. **e**

5. **e**

6. **b**

7. a

8. b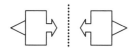

9. c

10. d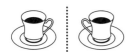

11. b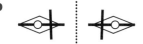

12. a

Section 2 Test 5 (pages 24–25)

1. e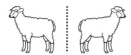

2. b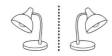

3. b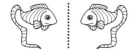

4. e

5. c

6. d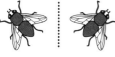

7. e The shape is reflected in the vertical mirror line.

8. b The shape is reflected in the horizontal mirror line.

9. c The shape is reflected in the horizontal mirror line.

10. a The same size shape is rotated 90° clockwise.

11. b The shape is rotated 90° anticlockwise.

12. d The shape is rotated 90° clockwise and changes from white to black.

Section 2 Test 6 (pages 26–27)

1. b The shape is reflected.

2. e The picture is reflected.

3. b The picture is reflected.

4. c The picture is reflected.

5. a The picture is reflected.

6. d The picture is reflected in the horizontal mirror line.

7. d Repeating pattern

8. b The shape gets smaller and lighter in colour.

9. a Repeating pattern

10. c One star is added each time.

11. c The shape is rotated 90° clockwise each time.

12. e One cross is taken away each time.

Answers

Section 3 Test 1 (pages 28–29)

1. **b** Each picture contains the same single-coloured outer shape with a white shape inside.
2. **a** Each picture contains a quadrilateral with three lines inside.
3. **d** Each picture gets darker in the middle.
4. **d** Each picture shows an arrow pointing into the shape.
5. **b** Each picture contains a large oval within the outer shape.
6. **c** Each picture contains a grey circle with two bent arrows.
7. **a** The others all have an outer shape.
8. **d** The others all have two grey squares and one white square.
9. **e** The others all have spots.
10. **a** The others all have two pieces of fruit.
11. **a** The others all have the same frame.
12. **e** The others all have stripes going in the same direction.

Section 3 Test 2 (pages 30–31)

1. **e** The shape has a much thicker outer line and changes from white to grey.
2. **c** The shapes swap colours.
3. **b** The shape has the same number of sides as the number of legs of the creature.
4. **c** A vertical reflection is added to the original shape.
5. **d** The picture is reflected in the vertical mirror line.
6. **b** The shape is halved horizontally and the colour changes from white to grey.
7. **a** The arrow is rotated 45° clockwise each time.
8. **c** Repeating pattern
9. **e** The picture gets smaller.
10. **b** One hexagon is added each time and the colours alternate.
11. **c** The shape gets smaller and lighter in colour.
12. **a** One rectangle is taken away each time and the colours alternate.

Section 3 Test 3 (pages 32–33)

1. **b**

2. **c**

3. **e**

4. **b**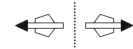

5. **a**

6. **b**

7. **b**

8. **d**

9. **b**

10. **a**

11. **e**

12. **c**

■ Section 3 Test 4 (pages 34–35)

1. **b** The picture is rotated 90° clockwise.
2. **c** The shape is reflected in the horizontal mirror line.
3. **d** The picture is reflected.
4. **a** The picture is reflected.
5. **d** The shape is rotated 90° clockwise and changes from black to grey with a black outline.
6. **e** The picture is reflected.
7. **e** Each picture contains an arrow pointing towards the shape.
8. **c** Each picture contains a speech or thought bubble.
9. **c** Each picture contains a wheel.
10. **b** Each picture contains single-headed arrows pointing right.
11. **b** Each picture contains two arrows.
12. **c** Each shape has five sides.

■ Section 3 Test 5 (pages 36–37)

1. **d** The others all have three lines.
2. **e** The others all have a white outer shape and black inner shapes.
3. **c** The others all have two lines crossing the arrow.
4. **c** The others all fade to white at the top.
5. **d** The others all have triangles at the top.
6. **b** The others all have white hexagons.
7. **a** The bottom shape is reflected in the horizontal mirror line.
8. **d** The shape changes to grey and has a shadow to the left.
9. **c** The picture is reflected in the horizontal mirror line.
10. **d** The arrow changes from straight to curved but still goes from top left to bottom right.
11. **b** The picture is reflected in the vertical mirror line.
12. **e** The picture has half the number of ovals and these change from black to grey.

■ Section 3 Test 6 (pages 38–39)

1. **d** Repeating pattern
2. **c** There is one less star each time.
3. **e** One circle is added each time.
4. **a** The arrow moves down the quadrilateral.
5. **b** The circle moves clockwise around the triangle.
6. **a** The picture is rotated 45° clockwise each time.
7. **b**
8. **e**
9. **d**
10. **b**
11. **c**
12. **d**

This book of answers is a pull-out section from
Rapid Reasoning Tests: Non-verbal Reasoning 2

Published by Schofield & Sims Ltd,
Dogley Mill, Fenay Bridge, Huddersfield HD8 0NQ, UK
Telephone 01484 607080
www.schofieldandsims.co.uk
Second impression 2014
Copyright © Schofield & Sims Ltd, 2014

Author: **Rebecca Brant**
Rebecca Brant has asserted her moral right under the Copyright, Designs and Patents Act, 1988, to be identified as the
author of this work.

British Library Cataloguing in Publication Data
A catalogue record for this book is available from the British Library.

Commissioned by **Carolyn Richardson Publishing Services** *(www.publiserve.co.uk)*

Design by **Oxford Designers & Illustrators**
Printed in the UK by **The Lavenham Press Ltd**, *Suffolk*

ISBN 978 07217 1227 7

■ Which picture on the right belongs to the group on the left? Circle the letter.

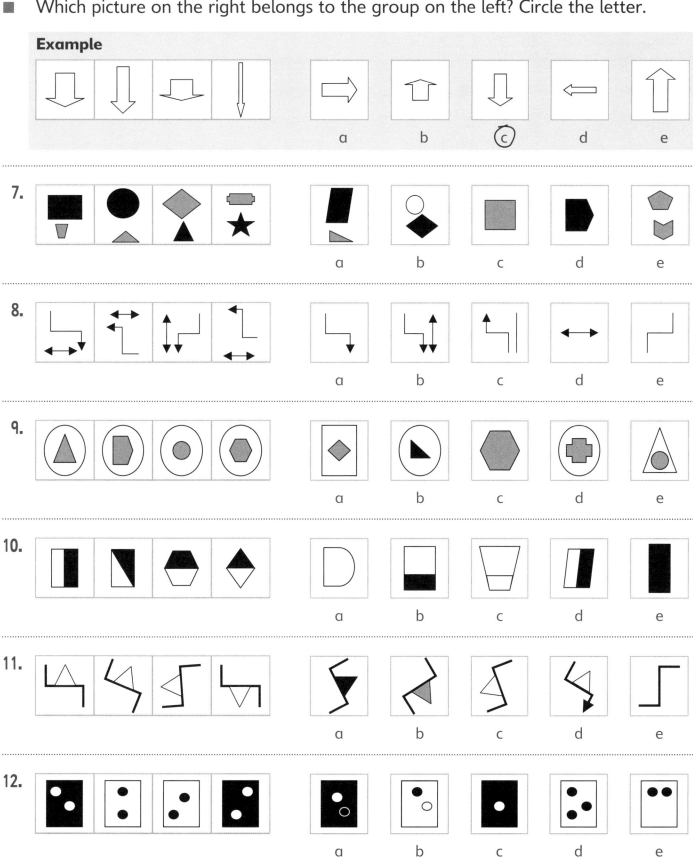

Example

a b c d e

7.

a b c d e

8.

a b c d e

9.

a b c d e

10.

a b c d e

11.

a b c d e

12.

a b c d e

End of test.

Score:	Time taken:	Target met?

Target time: **6 minutes**

In which picture on the right is the picture on the left hidden? Circle the letter.

Example

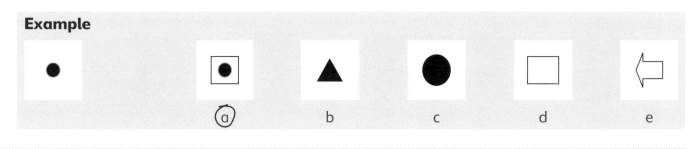

a b c d e

1.

a b c d e

2.

a b c d e

3.

a b c d e

4.

a b c d e

5.

a b c d e

6.

a b c d e

Now go on to the next page. ➡

■ Pretend the dotted line is a mirror. Which picture on the right is a reflection of the picture on the left? Circle the letter.

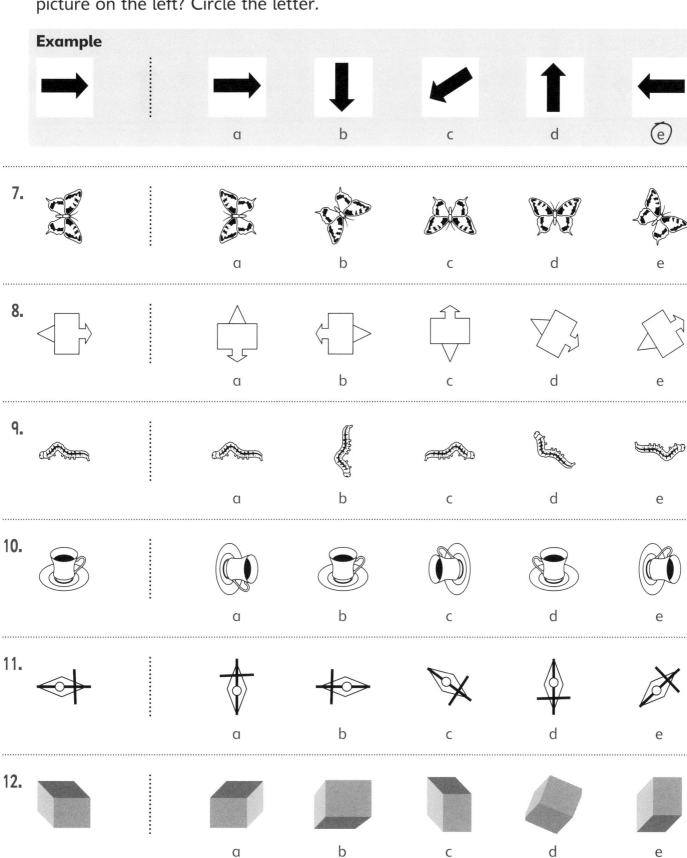

Example

a   b   c   d   e

7.

a   b   c   d   e

8.

a   b   c   d   e

9.

a   b   c   d   e

10.

a   b   c   d   e

11.

a   b   c   d   e

12.

a   b   c   d   e

End of test.

Score:	Time taken:	Target met?

Target time: **6 minutes**

Pretend the dotted line is a mirror. Which picture on the right is a reflection of the picture on the left? Circle the letter.

Example

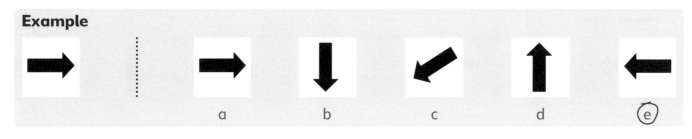

a   b   c   d   (e)

1.

a   b   c   d   e

2.

a   b   c   d   e

3.

a   b   c   d   e

4.

a   b   c   d   e

5.

a   b   c   d   e

6.

a   b   c   d   e

Now go on to the next page. ➜

■ Which of the pictures on the right best fits into the space in the grid? Circle the letter.

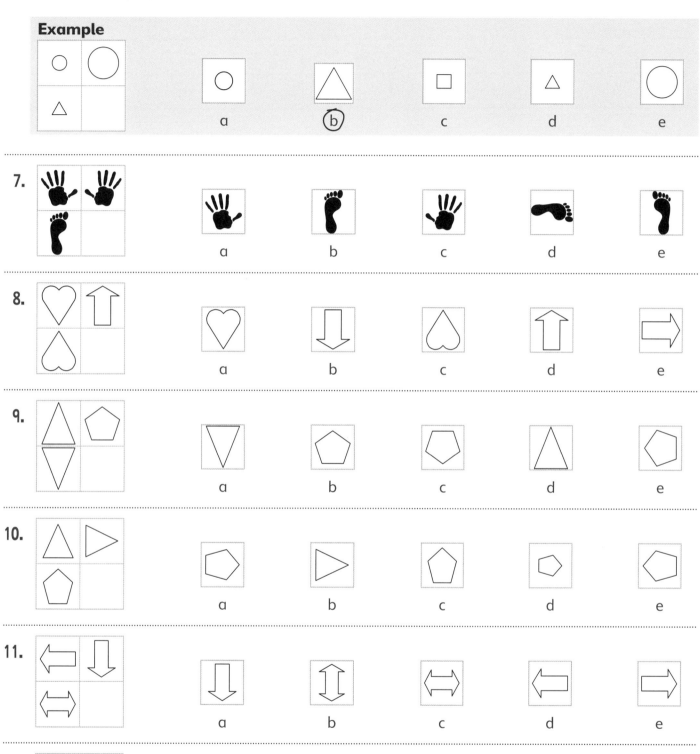

Example

7.

8.

9.

10.

11.

12.

End of test.

| Score: | | Time taken: | | Target met? | |

Which of the pictures on the right best fits into the space in the grid?
Circle the letter.

Example

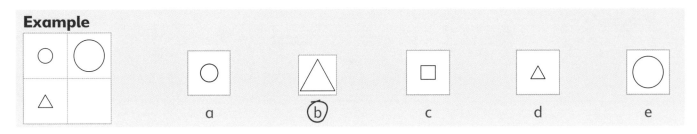

a   b   c   d   e

1.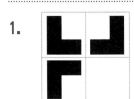

   a   b   c   d   e

2.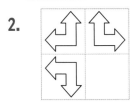

   a   b   c   d   e

3.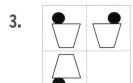

   a   b   c   d   e

4.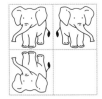

   a   b   c   d   e

5.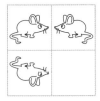

   a   b   c   d   e

6.

   a   b   c   d   e

Now go on to the next page. ➡

Which picture on the right goes in the empty space? Circle the letter.

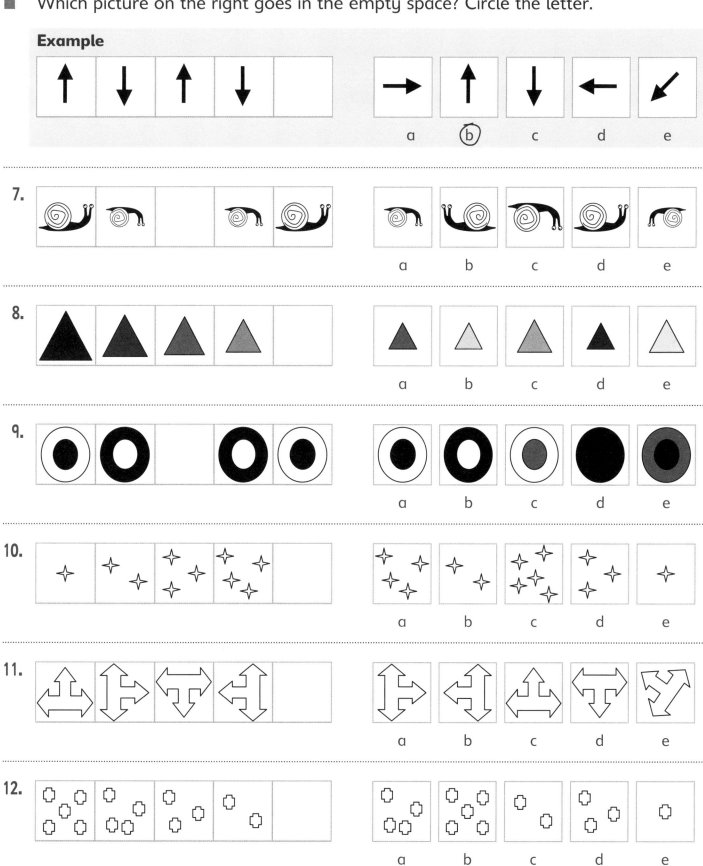

End of test.

Score:	Time taken:	Target met?

Which picture on the right belongs to the group on the left? Circle the letter.

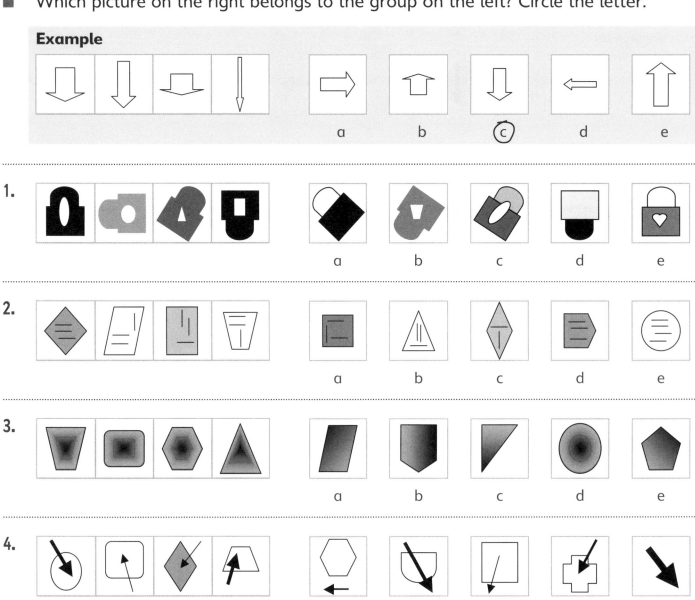

Example

a   b   ⓒ   d   e

1.

a   b   c   d   e

2.

a   b   c   d   e

3.

a   b   c   d   e

4.

a   b   c   d   e

5.
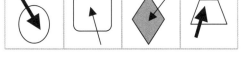

a   b   c   d   e

6.
   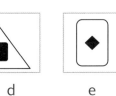

a   b   c   d   e

Now go on to the next page. ➔

■ Which picture is the odd one out? Circle the letter.

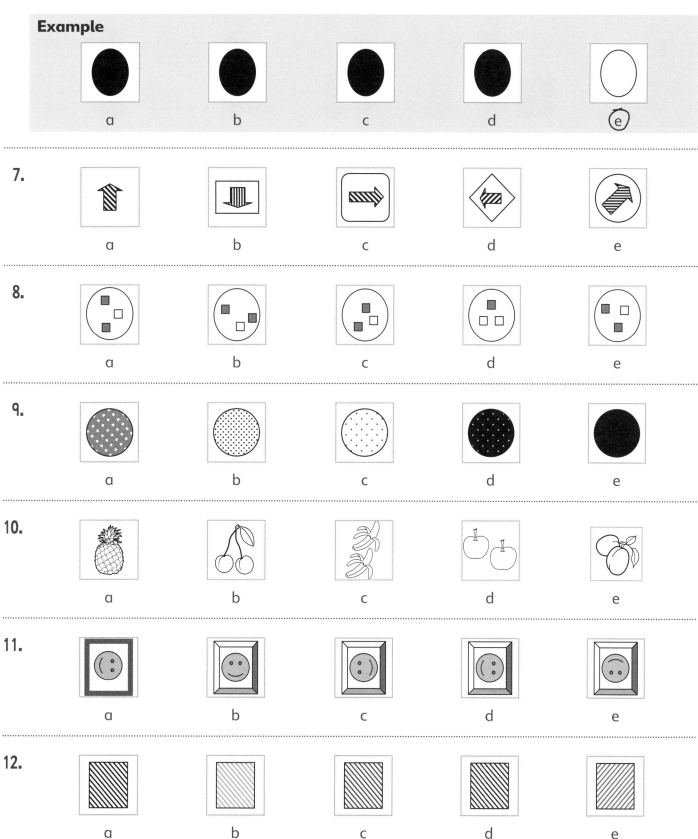

Example

| a | b | c | d | (e) |

7. | a | b | c | d | e |

8. | a | b | c | d | e |

9. | a | b | c | d | e |

10. | a | b | c | d | e |

11. | a | b | c | d | e |

12. | a | b | c | d | e |

End of test.

| Score: | Time taken: | Target met? |

Target time: 6 minutes

The first two pictures go together. Which of the five pictures on the right goes with the third picture in the same way? Circle the letter.

Example

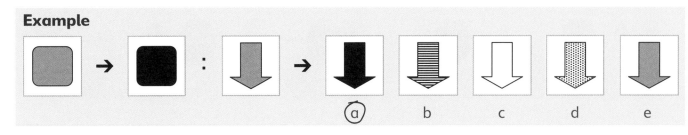

a   b   c   d   e

1.

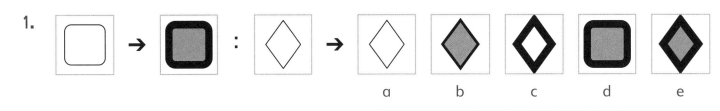

a   b   c   d   e

2.

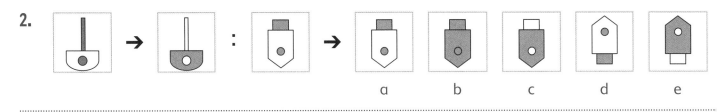

a   b   c   d   e

3.

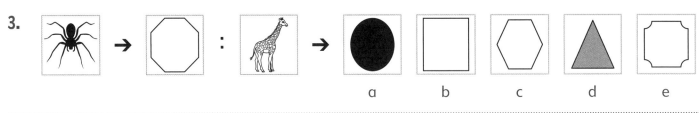

a   b   c   d   e

4.

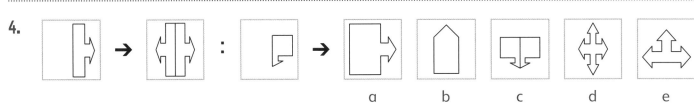

a   b   c   d   e

5.

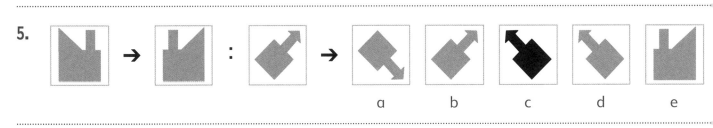

a   b   c   d   e

6.

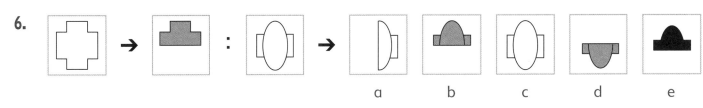

a   b   c   d   e

Now go on to the next page. ➡

■ Which picture on the right goes in the empty space? Circle the letter.

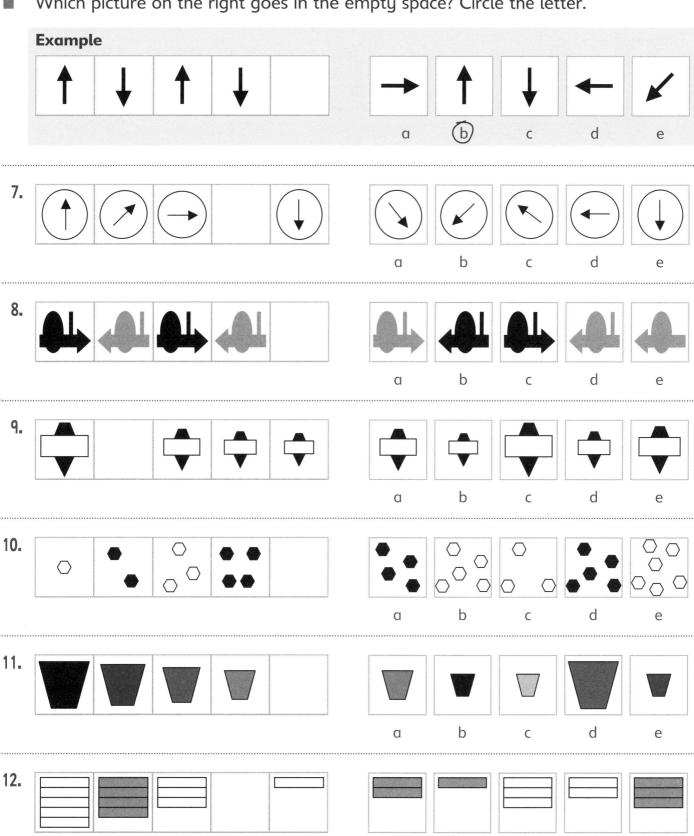

End of test.

| Score: | | Time taken: | | Target met? | |

In which picture on the right is the picture on the left hidden? Circle the letter.

Example

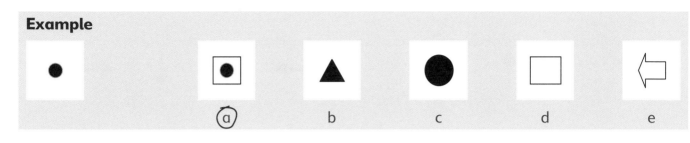

a   b   c   d   e

1.

a   b   c   d   e

2.

a   b   c   d   e

3.

a   b   c   d   e

4.

a   b   c   d   e

5.

a   b   c   d   e

6.

a   b   c   d   e

Now go on to the next page. ➡

■ Pretend the dotted line is a mirror. Which picture on the right is a reflection of the picture on the left? Circle the letter.

Example

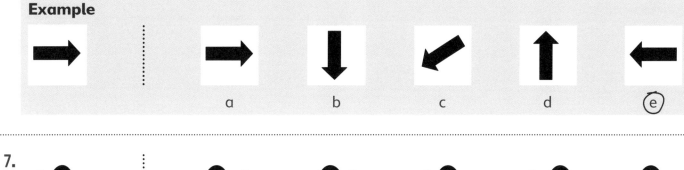

a   b   c   d   (e)

7.

a   b   c   d   e

8.   

a   b   c   d   e

9.   

a   b   c   d   e

10.

a   b   c   d   e

11.

a   b   c   d   e

12.

a   b   c   d   e

End of test.

Score:	Time taken:	Target met?

Which of the pictures on the right best fits into the space in the grid? Circle the letter.

Example

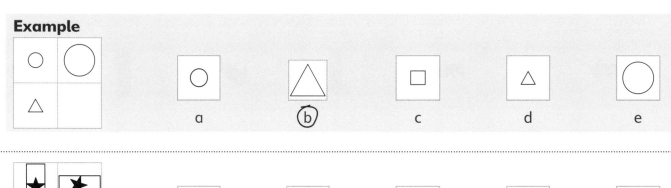

a   b   c   d   e

1.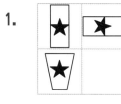

   a   b   c   d   e

2.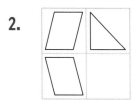

   a   b   c   d   e

3.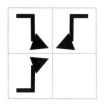

   a   b   c   d   e

4.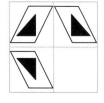

   a   b   c   d   e

5.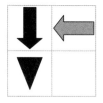

   a   b   c   d   e

6.

   a   b   c   d   e

Now go on to the next page. ➡

■ Which picture on the right belongs to the group on the left? Circle the letter.

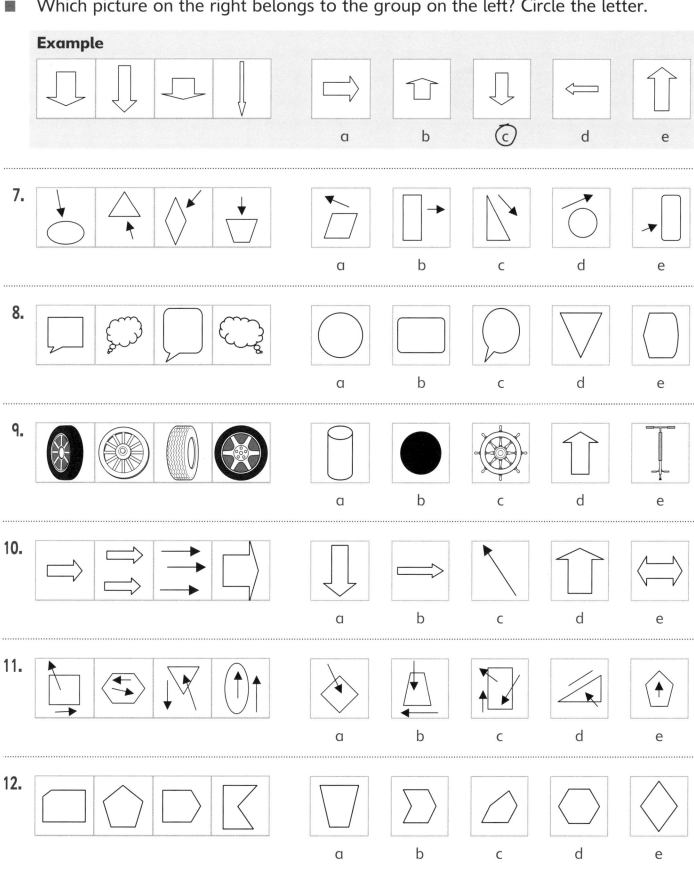

Example

| | | | | | a | b | c | d | e |

7.

8.

9.

10.

11.

12.

End of test.

Which picture is the odd one out? Circle the letter.

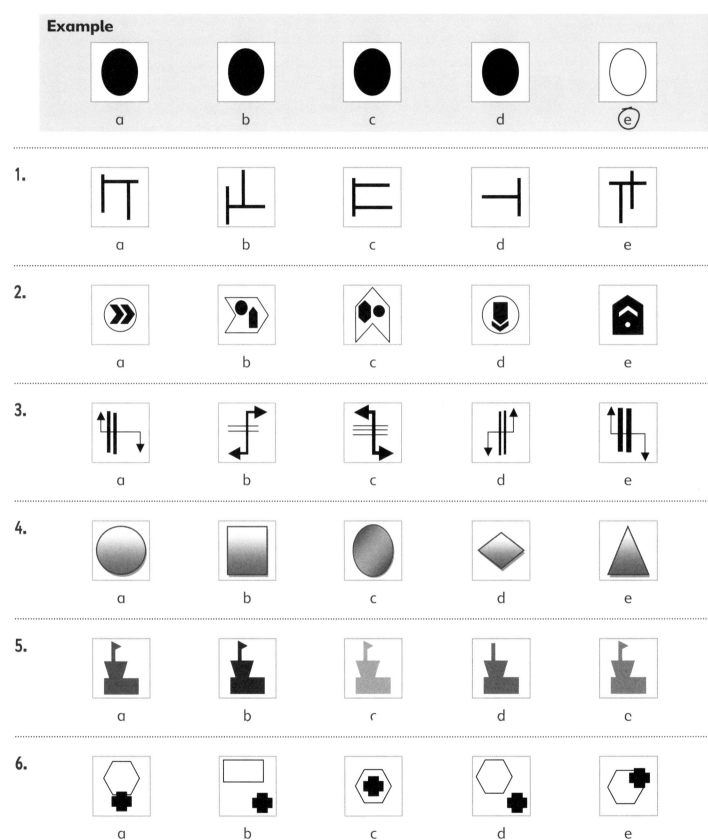

Example

a   b   c   d   e

1.

a   b   c   d   e

2.

a   b   c   d   e

3.

a   b   c   d   e

4.

a   b   c   d   e

5.

a   b   c   d   e

6.

a   b   c   d   e

Now go on to the next page. ➡

■ The first two pictures go together. Which of the five pictures on the right goes with the third picture in the same way? Circle the letter.

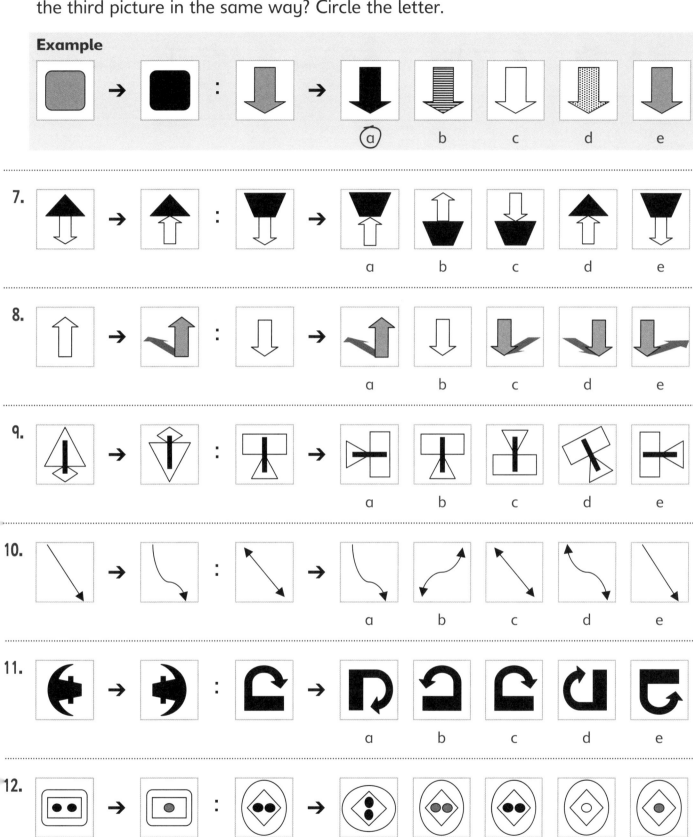

Example

7.

8.

9.

10.

11.

12.

End of test.

■ Which picture on the right goes in the empty space? Circle the letter.

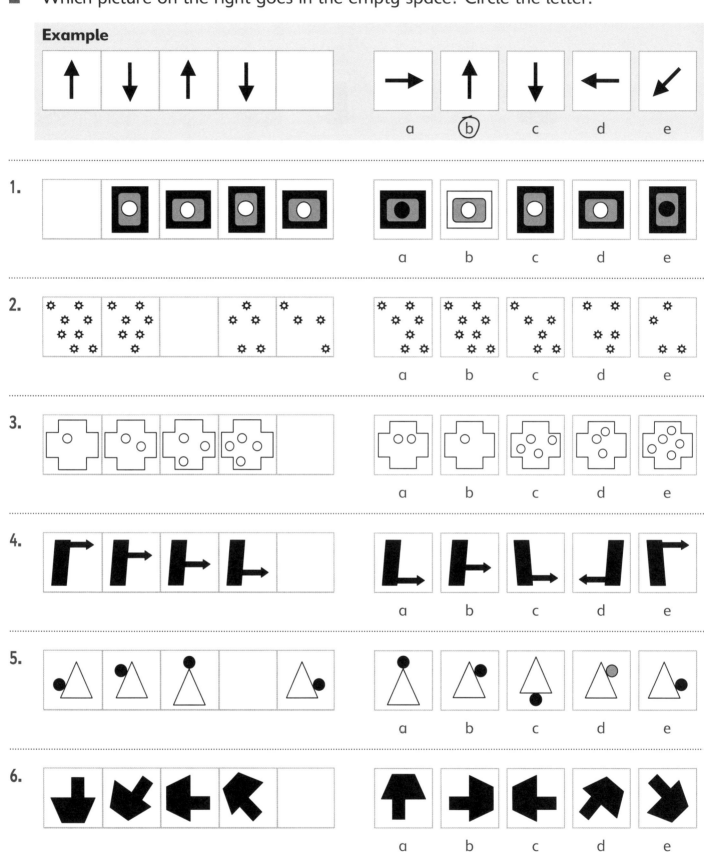

Now go on to the next page. ➜

■ In which picture on the right is the picture on the left hidden? Circle the letter.

Example

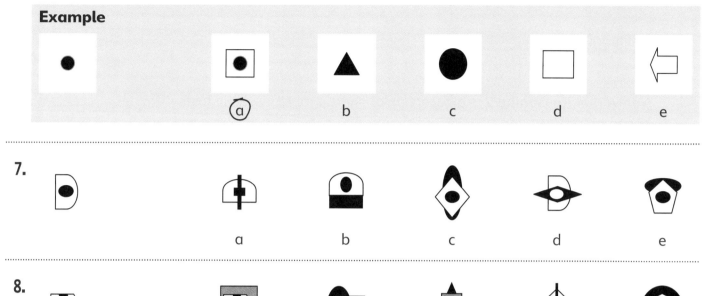

a   b   c   d   e

7.

a   b   c   d   e

8.

a   b   c   d   e

9.

a   b   c   d   e

10.

a   b   c   d   e

11.

a   b   c   d   e

12.

a   b   c   d   e

End of test.

Score:	Time taken:	Target met?

Non-verbal Reasoning 2

Non-verbal Reasoning 2 is a collection of short, problem-solving tests based on pictures and patterns. Each timed test includes age-appropriate questions, providing opportunities for children to practise and master non-verbal reasoning skills in preparation for the 11+ and other school selection tests. This book is part of the **Rapid Reasoning Tests** series and covers the following question types: similarities and differences; missing and hidden shapes; cubes, codes and combinations.

Rapid Reasoning Tests provides short, effective, timed tests in reasoning. The series comprises six books of verbal reasoning tests and six books of non-verbal reasoning tests.

Written by experienced teachers and designed for independent use, **Rapid Reasoning Tests** has been carefully structured to provide practice of key, standard format question types. Each collection of tests has been designed for use over one year and provides one section per term in order to support regular practice.

Key features

- **Short tests** requiring few resources that are easy to fit into a busy timetable.
- A **target time** for each test encourages children to work quickly and develop the necessary exam skills for success in the 11+ and other tests.
- **Pull-out answers** in the centre of each book can be easily removed.
- **Free downloads** to support the series are available from the Schofield & Sims website.

The full series includes the following books:

MIX
Paper from responsible sources
FSC www.fsc.org FSC® C010693

ISBN 978-07217-1227-7

9 780721 712277 >

ISBN 978 07217 1227 7

Key Stage 2

Age range 7–8

£3.95

(Retail price)

For further information and to place an order visit
www.schofieldandsims.co.uk or telephone 01484 607080